AUTUMN SNOW

FLITZYOOKS .COM™

FLITZY BOOKS .COM™

Where love and imagination flit, flutter, and fly!

Visit http://www.flitzybooks.com
for FREE activities, video books, and more!

Dedicated to the reader...

that you may enjoy the autumn snow that falls in your neighborhood.

"Mom it's the season for making snowballs."

"The season for hills and GIGANTIC snow walls!"

"Mom look outside, then you'll see what
I know! That leaves on trees make crisp

AUTUMN SNOW!"

Ginger runs to the window
and looks out its top.

She beams at the trees and
the COLORS they drop.

First she sees Maple-
a red orang-ish snow.

Then comes Pin Oak with
a scarlet bronze show.

Next, a White Ash
dumps yellow quite swift.

Followed by Sweet Gum with
a soft purple snow drift.

"Come on little Tommy, let's go out and play!
Let's jump and hide in the snow all day!"
They step in their boots and zip up their jackets.
They run out the door making all sorts of racket.

"Ok little Tommy,
now lay on the ground.
DO NOT make a move and
DO NOT make a sound."
Tommy nods his head and
goes down in a leap.
He goes stiff as a board,
not making a peep.

"Alright little Tommy,
now close your eyes.
I am gonna cover you up

about a mile **HIGH!**"
Ginger flies to the shed
and gets the wheelbarrow.
She loads it with snow
while singing a carol.

She returns with
her load and dumps
it real slow.
She covers Tommy
up to every last toe!

"Ok little Tommy are you ready for fun?
Do something wild when you hear
number...

ONE!"

Slowly she counts to her magic number. And awakens Tommy from his snowy slumber.

Three...
Two...
ONE!!!!!

Ginger scratches her head
then says with a clap.

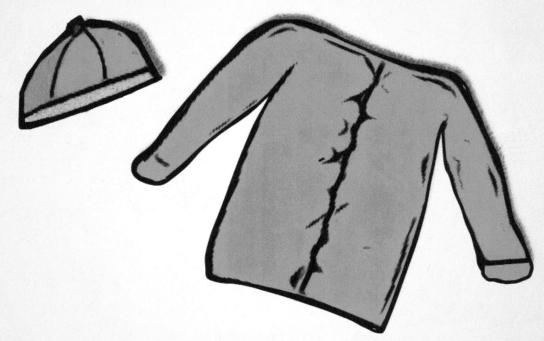

"I know! Tommy take off your
red jacket and cap!"

Next Ginger strikes a strange leafy pose.
Then she makes a fat man with a pinecone nose.

Tommy smiles at the man and dresses him quick.
He giggles and wiggles at their Autumn St. Nick.

"Oh, Ginger, he's perfect!
He's my little leaf buddy!
Who cares that he's
slightly lop-sided and
really quite muddy!"

"Alright little Tommy, it's time to make shapes!

We must gather the snow— every last scrape!"

Together they rake the autumn snowflakes. The leaves crinkle and wrinkle with every rake shake.

"Ok little Tommy, let's lay on the ground! And make snow angels colored yellowish-brown!"

All afternoon they play in the autumn snow. Never wanting to leave. never wanting to go.

When all of a sudden they hear mom at the door.

It's time to come in and do night time chores!

Although their fun is over they go in with a grin.

Because they know tomorrow they'll do it again.

For crisp autumn snow has one final trick....

It's the kind of snow that NEVER melts, but really likes to stick!

Hi! My name is Eve, and I am the author and creator of Autumn Snow. One of the things I like to do when I create picture books is use both drawings and real life photos.
I challenge you to go back through the pages and see if you can identify what is real in my illustrations. When you think you've found them all, turn the next page to see if you were right.

Good luck!

Our back door at Ft. Leavenworth, Kansas

Inside our house at Ft. Leavenworth, Kansas

Jake the rake

Fall Trees 2013 Fort Dix, New Jersey

Rusty old wheelbarrel

Fort Leavenworth, Kansas

Harry & Larry Halloween 2013

Old colorful curtain from Grandma

random pine cone

TV stand made by Grandpa and TV

Flitzy Rhyming Books!!

CPSIA information can be obtained
at www.ICGtesting.com
Printed in the USA
BVHW020405151021
618838BV00004B/59